Swing

D1545359

Wise Publications
London/New York/Paris/Sydney/
Copenhagen/Madrid

Exclusive Distributors:
Music Sales Limited
8/9 Frith Street, London W1V 5TZ, England.
Music Sales Pty Limited
120 Rothschild Avenue, Rosebery, NSW 2018, Australia.

This book © Copyright 1996 by Wise Publications
Order No. AM936925
ISBN 0-7119-5737-1

Cover design by Hutton & Partners
Compiled by Peter Evans
Music arranged by Stephen Duro
Music processed by Allegro Reproductions

Cover photograph courtesy of Zefa

Your Guarantee of Quality:
As publishers, we strive to produce every book to the highest commercial standards.

The music has been freshly engraved and the book has been carefully designed to minimise awkward page turns and to make playing from it a real pleasure.

Particular care has been given to specifying acid-free, neutral-sized paper made from pulps which have not been elemental chlorine bleached. This pulp is from farmed sustainable forests and was produced with special regard for the environment.
Throughout, the printing and binding have been planned to ensure a sturdy, attractive publication which should give years of enjoyment.

If your copy fails to meet our high standards, please inform us and we will gladly replace it.

Music Sales' complete catalogue lists thousands of titles and is free from your local music shop, or direct from Music Sales Limited. Please send a cheque/postal order for £1.50 for postage to: Music Sales Limited, Newmarket Road, Bury St. Edmunds, Suffolk IP33 3YB.

Visit the Internet Music Shop at
http://www.musicsales.co.uk

Printed in the United Kingdom by
Halstan & Co Limited, Amersham, Buckinghamshire.

Can't Help Lovin' Dat Man

Music by Jerome Kern. Words by Oscar Hammerstein II

Moderately

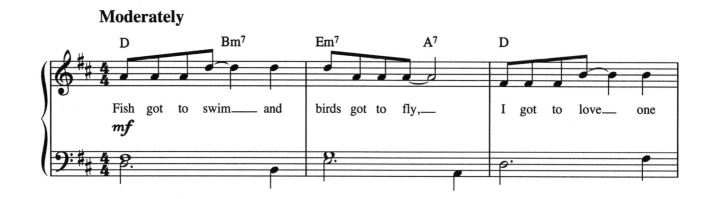

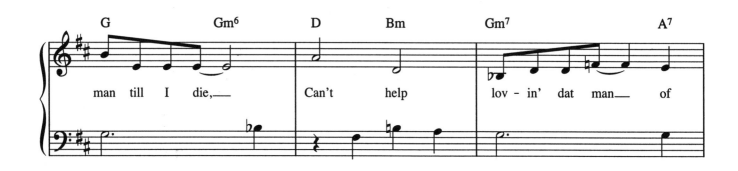

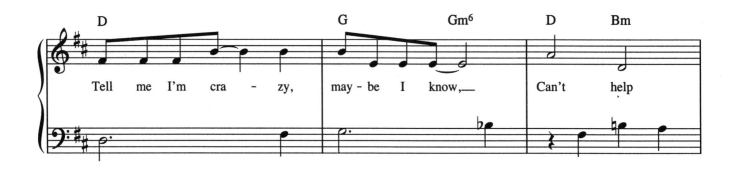

I'm Gettin' Sentimental Over You

Words by Ned Washington. Music by Geo. Bassman

Moderately

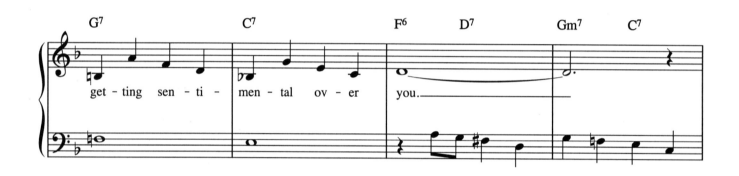

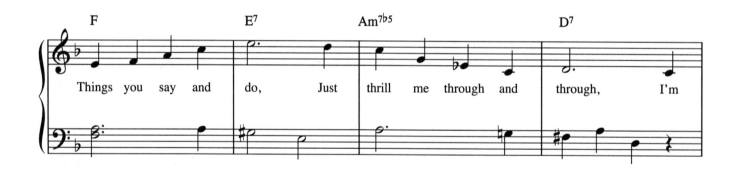

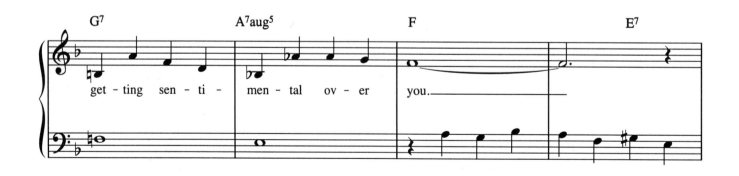

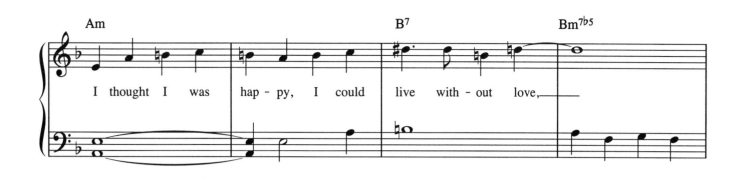

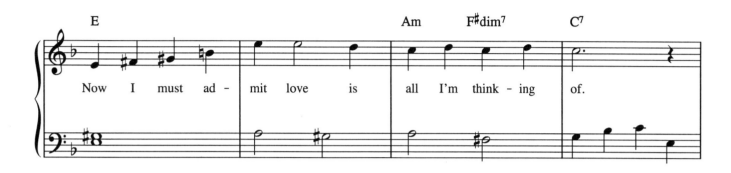

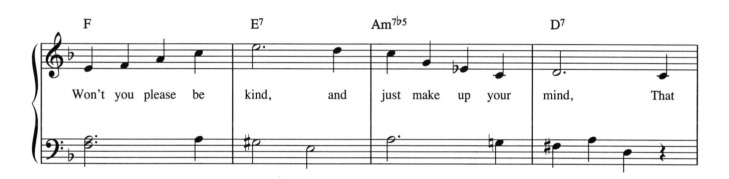

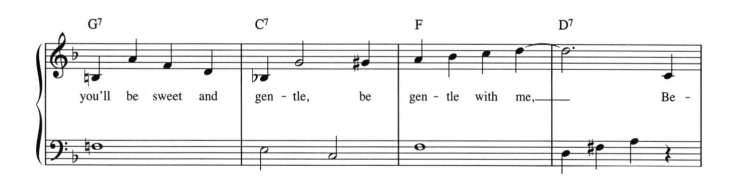

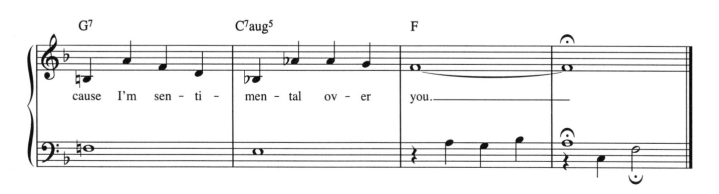

I Should Care

Words & Music by Sammy Cahn, Axel Stordahl & Paul Weston

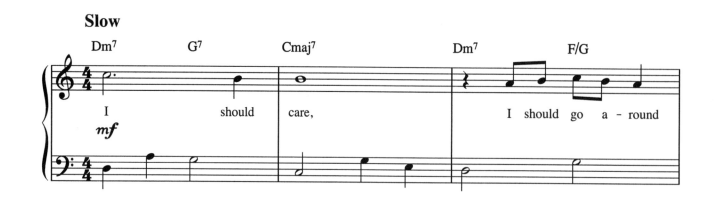

I should care, I should go a-round

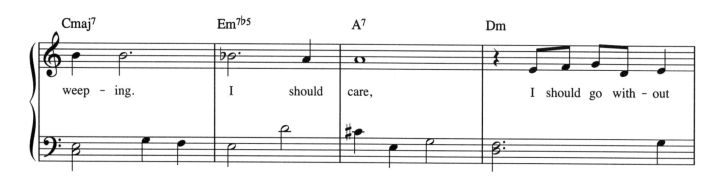

weep-ing. I should care, I should go with-out

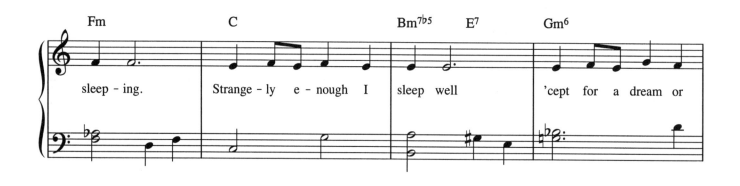

sleep-ing. Strange-ly e-nough I sleep well 'cept for a dream or

two, but then I count my sheep well. Fun-ny how sheep can

In The Mood

Words by Andy Razaf. Music by Joe Garland

Moderate swing

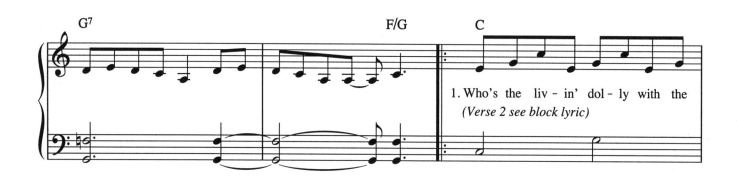

1. Who's the liv - in' dol - ly with the
(Verse 2 see block lyric)

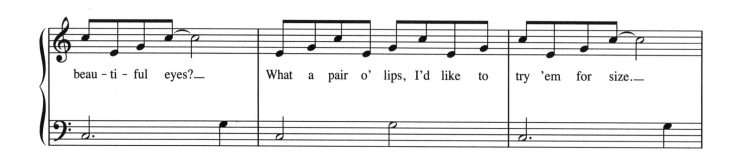

beau - ti - ful eyes?— What a pair o' lips, I'd like to try 'em for size.—

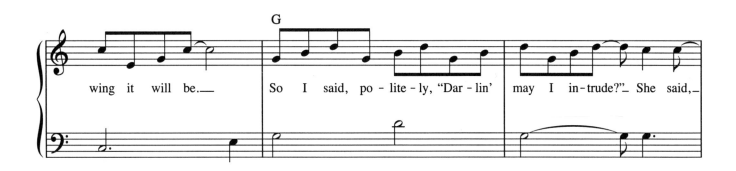

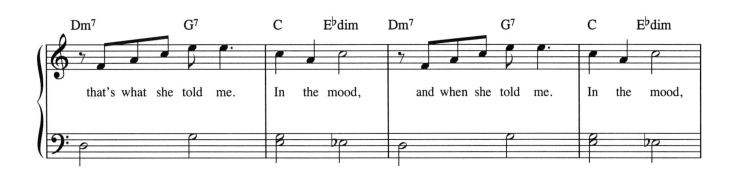

Verse 2:

First I held her lightly, and we started to dance,
Than I held her tightly, what a dreamy romance.
And I said, "Hey baby, it's a quarter to three;
There's a mess of moonlight, won't-cha share it with me?"
"Well" she answered, "Mister don't-cha know that it's rude
To keep my two lips waitin' when they're in the mood?"

In the mood, for all her kissin'.
In the mood, her crazy lovin'.
In the mood, what I was missin'.
It didn't take me long to say, "I'm in the mood now!"

It Don't Mean A Thing
(If It Ain't Got That Swing)

Words by Irving Mills. Music by Duke Ellington

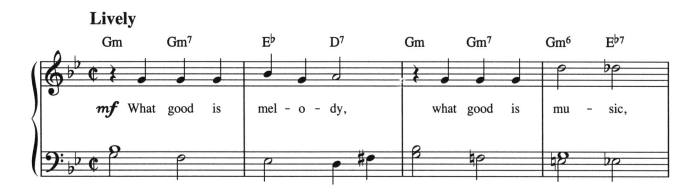

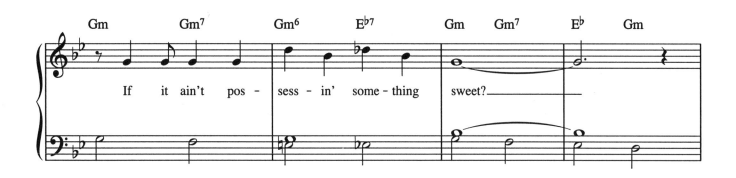

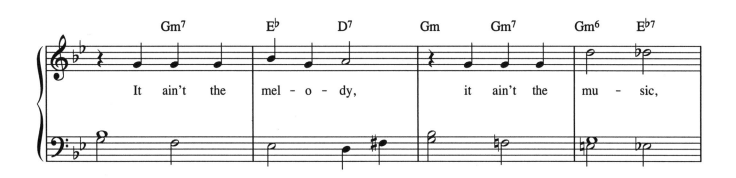

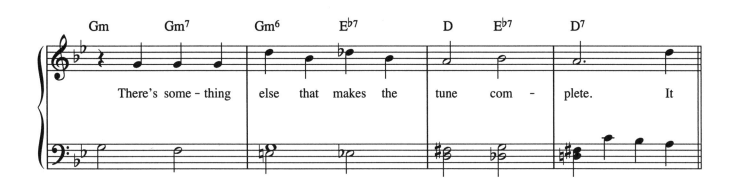

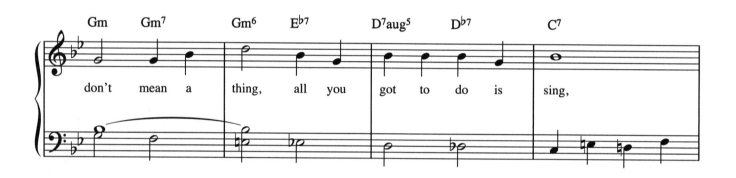

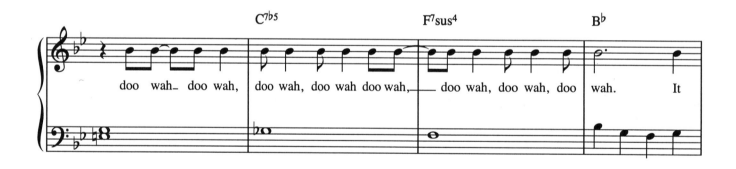

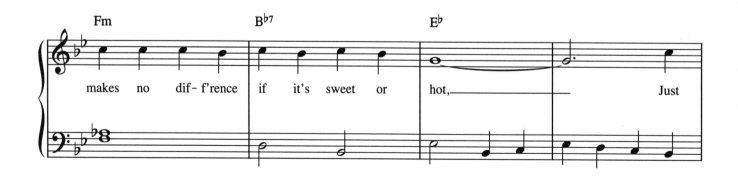

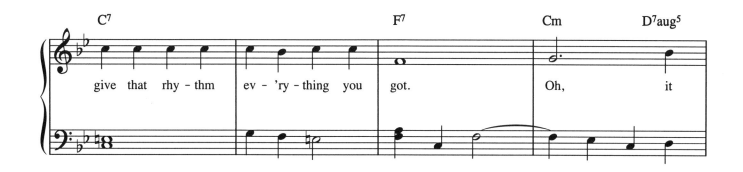

give that rhy-thm ev-'ry-thing you got. Oh, it

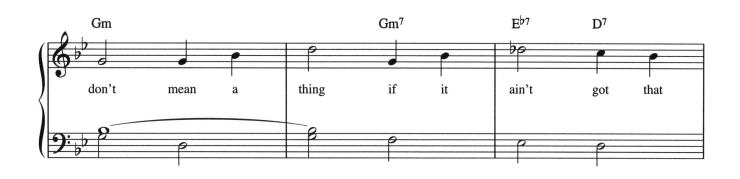

don't mean a thing if it ain't got that

swing, doo wah___ doo wah, doo wah, doo wah doo wah___

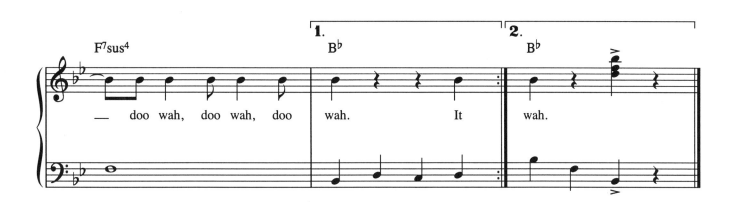

___ doo wah, doo wah, doo wah. It wah.

Lazy River

Words & Music by Hoagy Carmichael & Sidney Arodin

Moderately

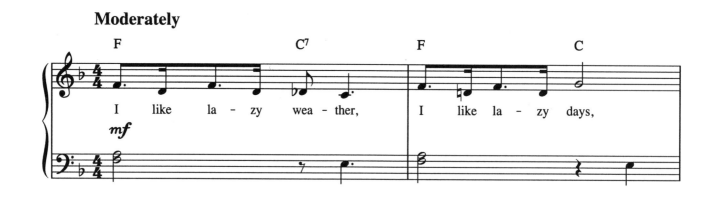

I like la - zy wea - ther, I like la - zy days,

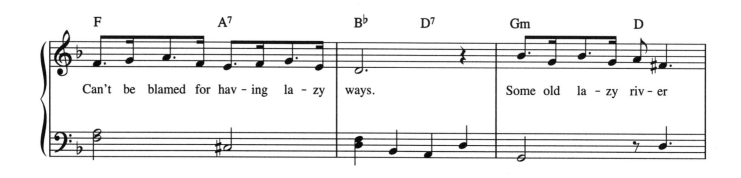

Can't be blamed for hav - ing la - zy ways. Some old la - zy riv - er

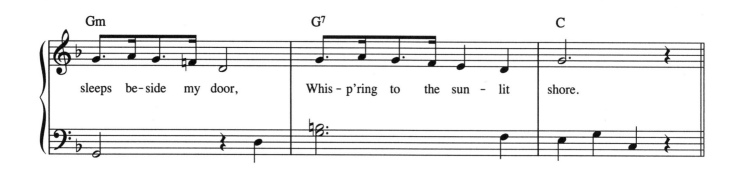

sleeps be - side my door, Whis - p'ring to the sun - lit shore.

Up a la - zy riv - er by the old mill - run, That la - zy, la - zy riv - er in the

Little Brown Jug

Traditional

Medium swing

Night Train

Words by Oscar Washington and Lewis C. Simpkins
Music by Jimmy Forrest

Moderately

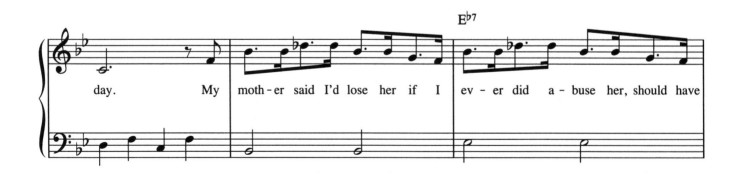

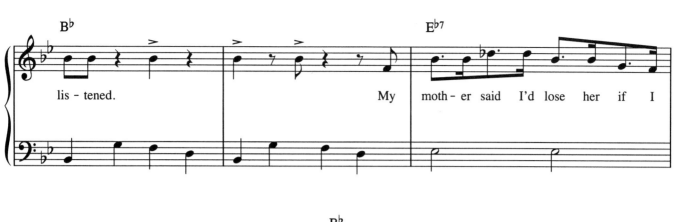

lis - tened. My moth- er said I'd lose her if I

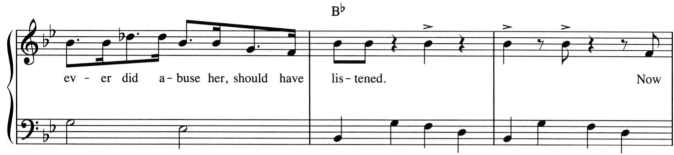

ev - er did a- buse her, should have lis - tened. Now

I have learned my les - son, my sweet ba - by was a bless - in', should have

lis - tened. Night Train, your

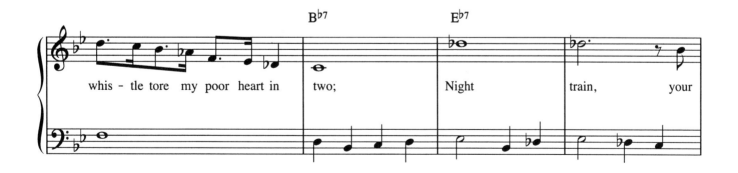

whis - tle tore my poor heart in two; Night train, your

whis - tle tore my poor heart in two, She's

gone, and I don't know what I'm gon - na do. It's

blue Mon - day morn - ing_____ she left me last_____ Sat - ur - day

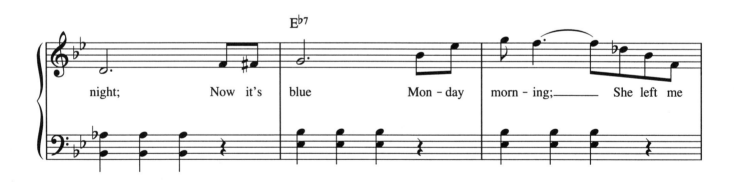

night; Now it's blue Mon - day morn - ing;_____ She left me

last_____ Sat - ur - day night; Ev - 'ry time I hear

trains blow_____ I get the blues;_____ Can't sleep at night.

Night train, Please bring my ba - by back home to

me; Night train, Please

bring my ba - by back home to me; She's

gone; The blues she left just won't set me free._____

On The Sunny Side Of The Street

Words by Dorothy Fields. Music by Jimmy McHugh

Moderately

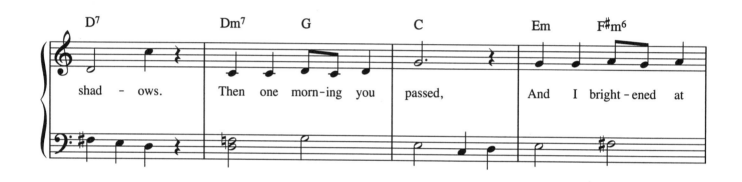

way   When you taught me how to   say: Grab your

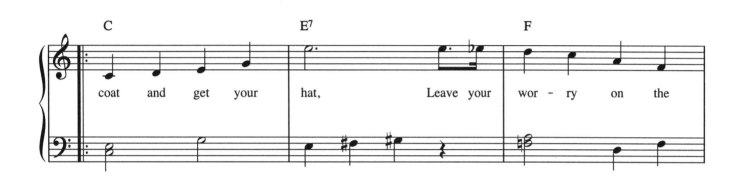

coat and get your hat,   Leave your wor - ry on the

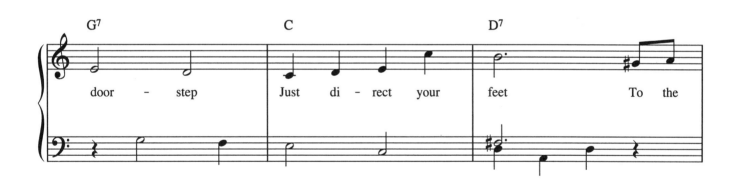

door - step   Just di - rect your feet   To the

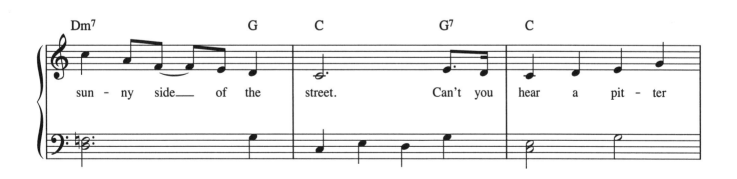

sun - ny side of the street.   Can't you hear a pit - ter

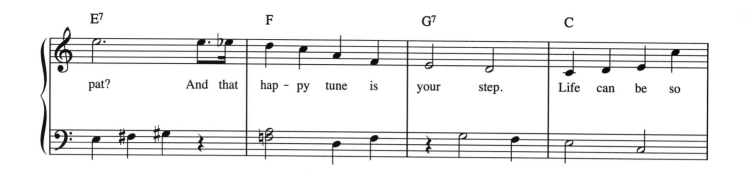

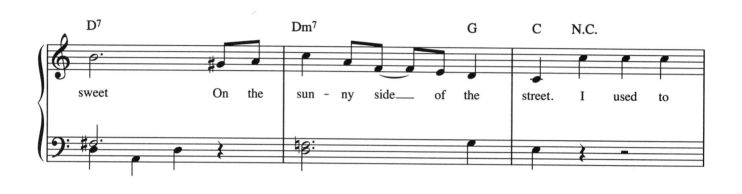

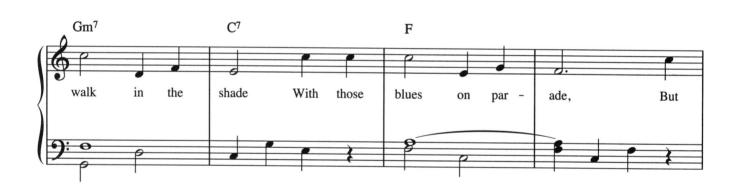

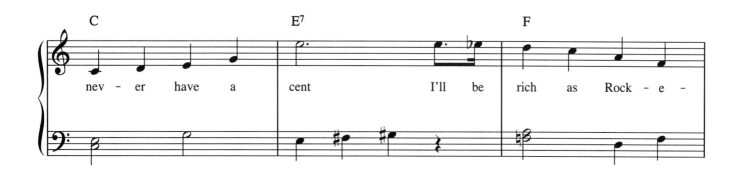

never have a cent I'll be rich as Rock-e-

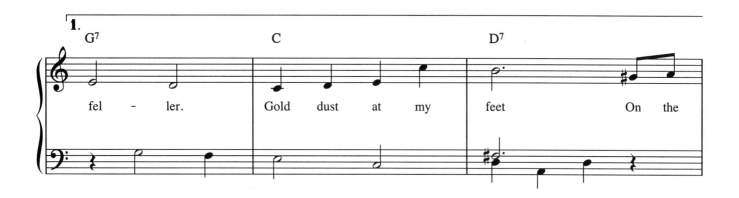

1.

fel - ler. Gold dust at my feet On the

sun - ny side_ of the street. Grab your

2.

fel - ler. Gold dust at my

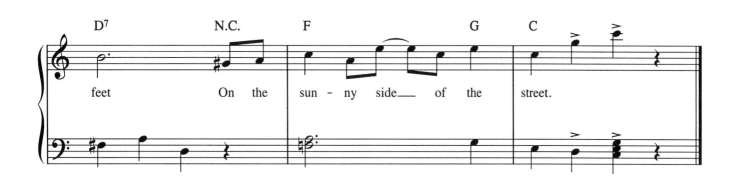

feet On the sun - ny side_ of the street.

Pennies From Heaven

Words by John Burke. Music by Arthur Johnston

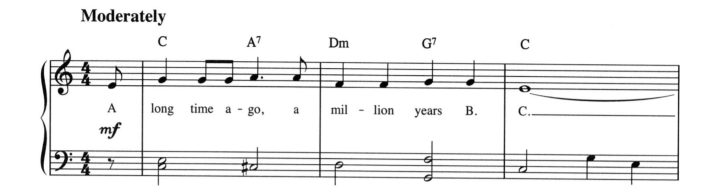

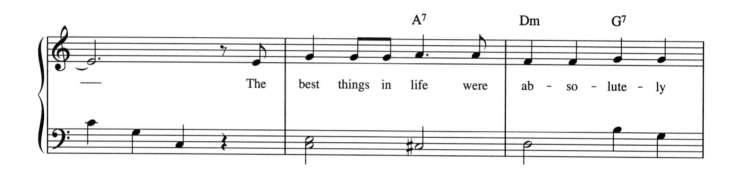

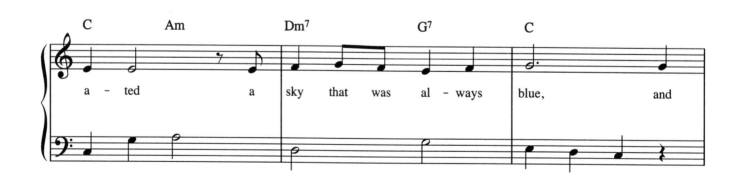

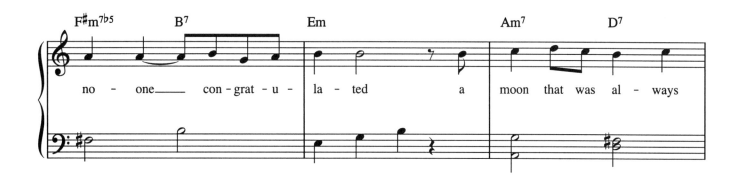

no - one____ con - grat - u - la - ted a moon that was al - ways

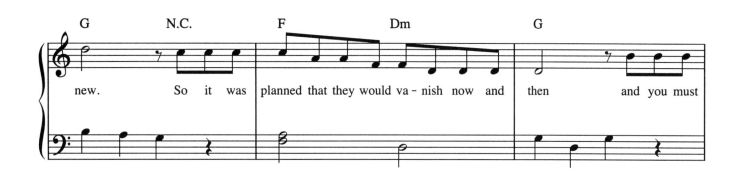

new. So it was planned that they would va - nish now and then and you must

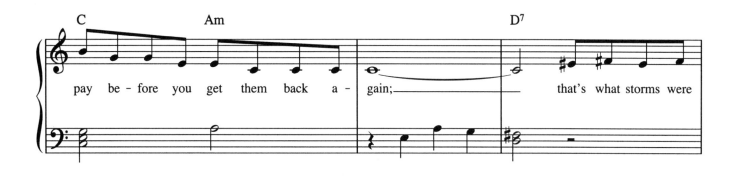

pay be - fore you get them back a - gain;____ that's what storms were

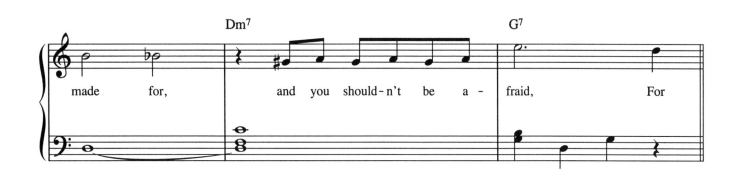

made for, and you should - n't be a - fraid, For

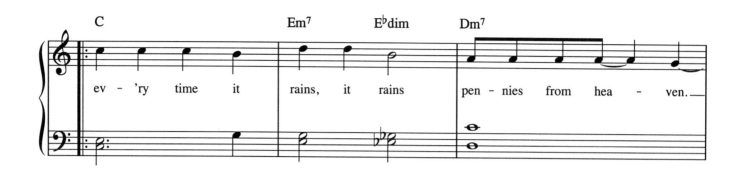

ev - 'ry time it rains, it rains pen - nies from hea - ven. —

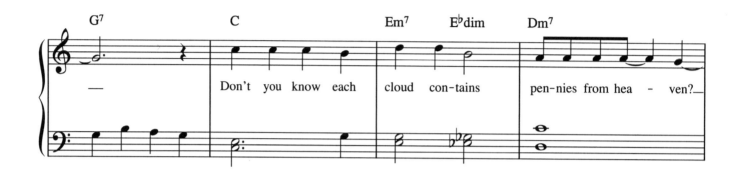

— Don't you know each cloud con-tains pen-nies from hea - ven? —

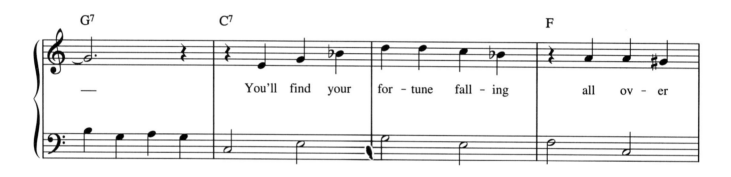

— You'll find your for - tune fall - ing all ov - er

town. Be sure that your um - brel - la

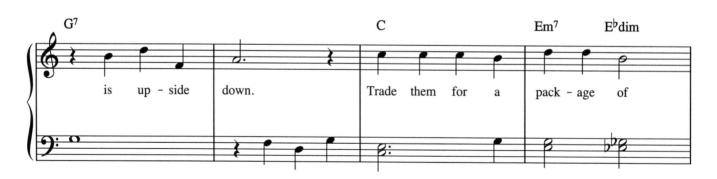

is up - side down. Trade them for a pack - age of

Pick Yourself Up

Music by Jerome Kern. Words by Dorothy Fields

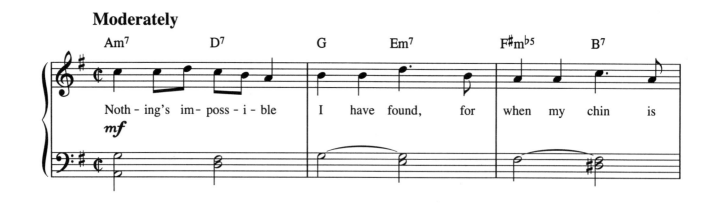

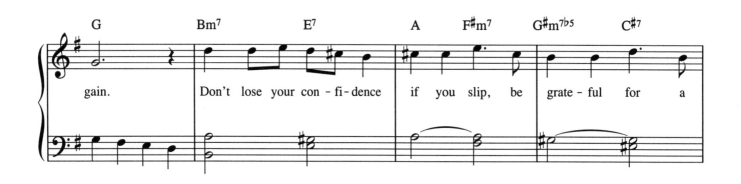

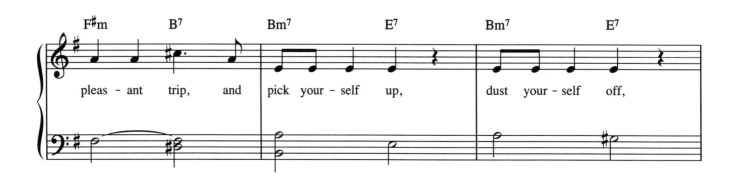

Tequila

Words & Music by Chuck Rio

Moderately

The Last Time I Saw Paris

Music by Jerome Kern. Words by Oscar Hammerstein II

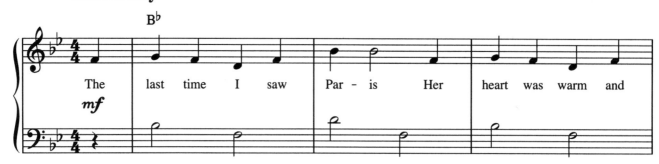

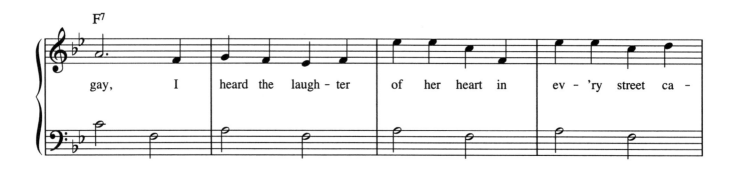

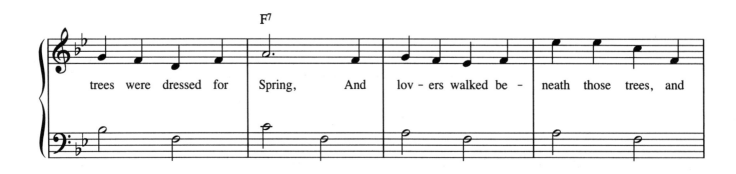

birds found songs to sing. I dodged the same old tax - i cabs that

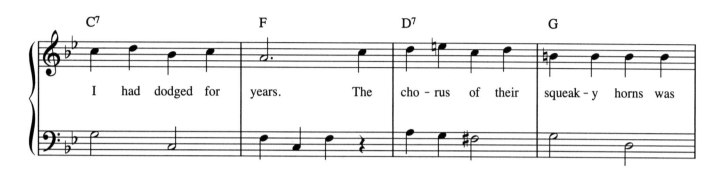

I had dodged for years. The cho - rus of their squeak - y horns was

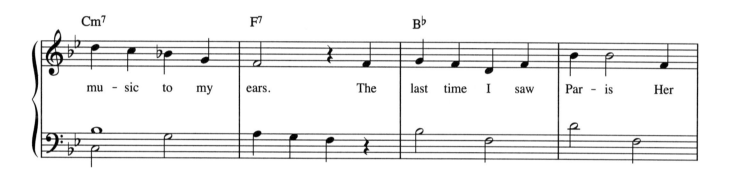

mu - sic to my ears. The last time I saw Par - is Her

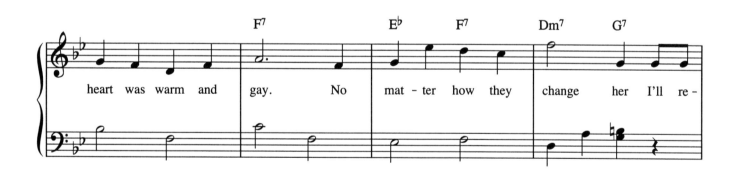

heart was warm and gay. No mat - ter how they change her I'll re -

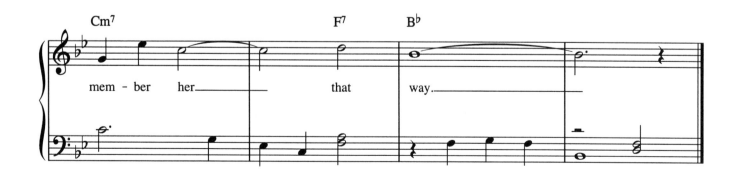

mem - ber her_____ that way._____

The Lonesome Road

Words by Gene Austin. Music by Nathaniel Shilkret

Moderately

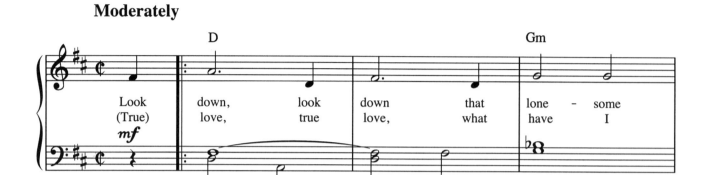

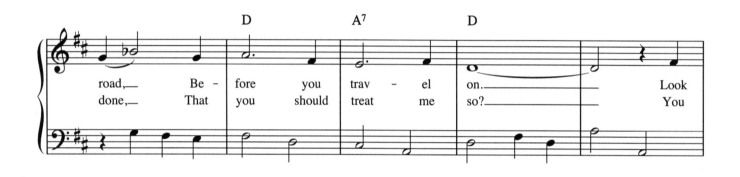

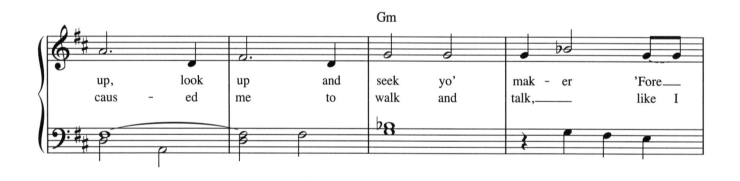

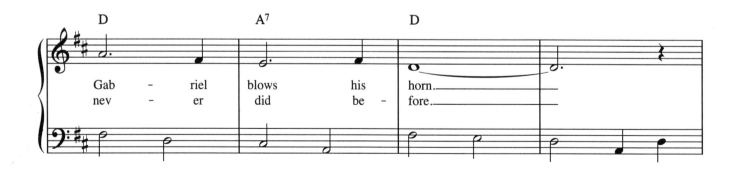

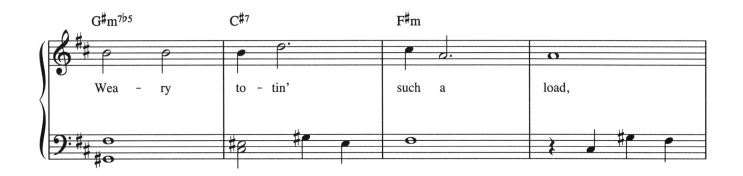

Wea - ry to - tin' such a load,

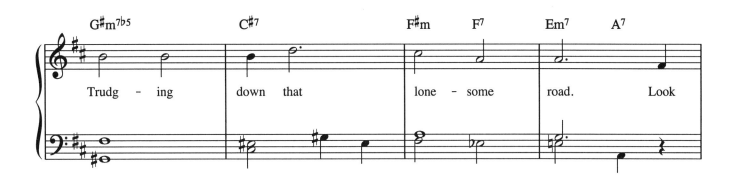

Trudg - ing down that lone - some road. Look

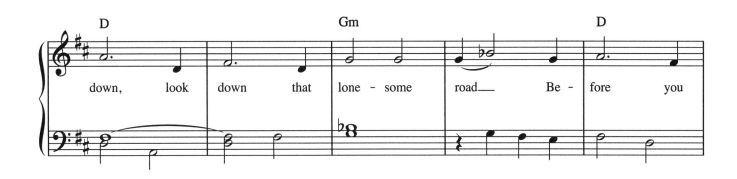

down, look down that lone - some road___ Be - fore you

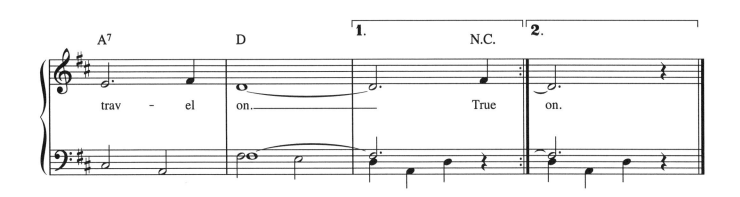

trav - el on.___ True on.

Moonlight Serenade

Words by Mitchell Parish. Music by Glenn Miller

stars_____ are a - glow_____ and to - night__ how their light__ sets me

dream - ing, My love,_____ do you know_____ that your

eyes__ are like stars__ bright - ly beam - ing? I bring you and

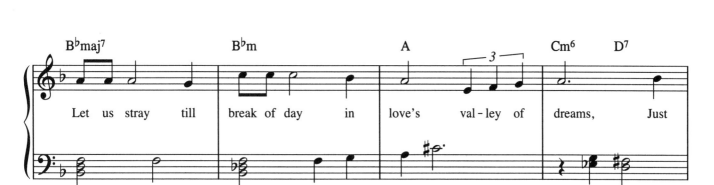

sing you a moon - light ser - e - nade.

Let us stray till break of day in love's val - ley of dreams, Just

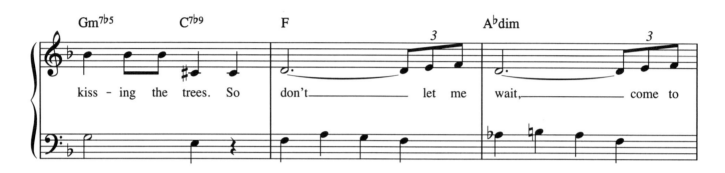

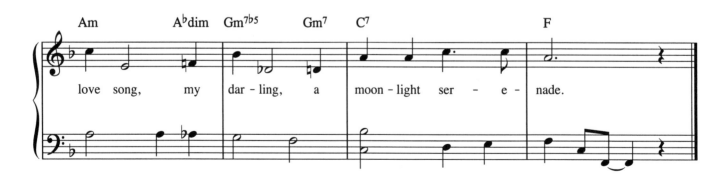

Tuxedo Junction

Words by Buddy Feyne
Music by Erskine Hawkins, William Johnson & Julian Dash

Medium swing

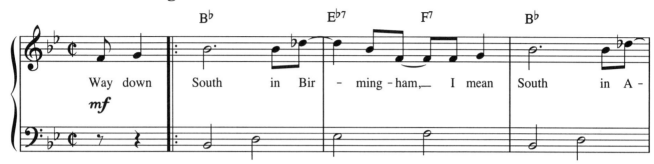

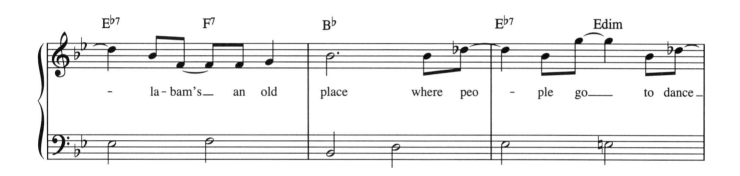

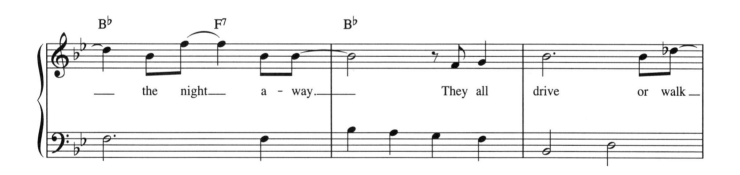

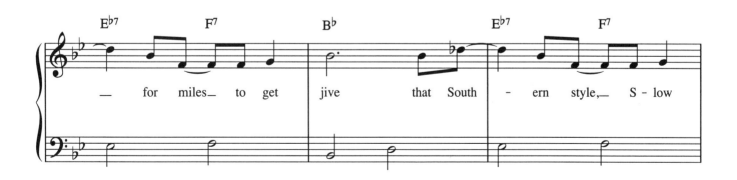

43

jive　　that makes＿　you want＿　to dance＿　'til break＿　of day.＿

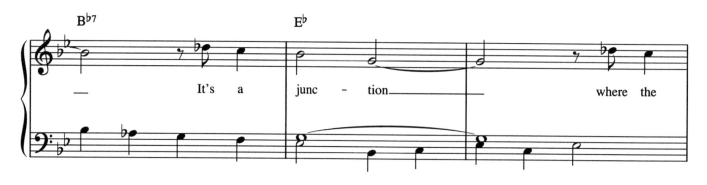

＿　It's　a　junc - tion＿　where the

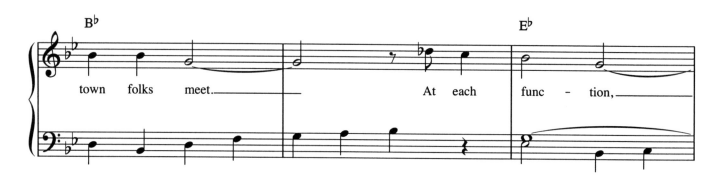

town　folks　meet.＿　＿　At each　func - tion,＿

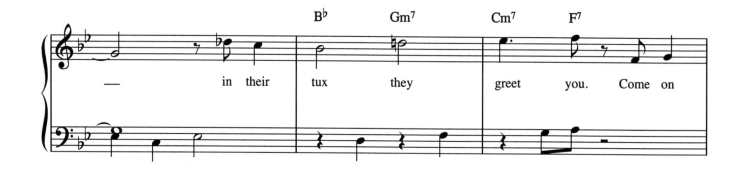

＿　in their　tux　they　greet　you.　Come on

down,　for - get＿　your care.＿　Come on　down,　you'll find＿

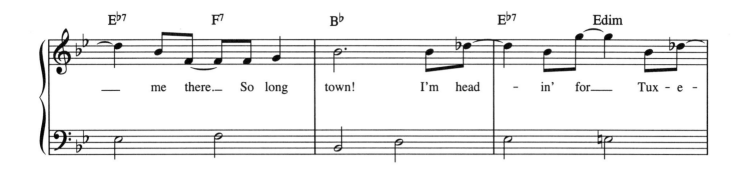

me there.＿ So long town! I'm head – in' for＿ Tux – e –

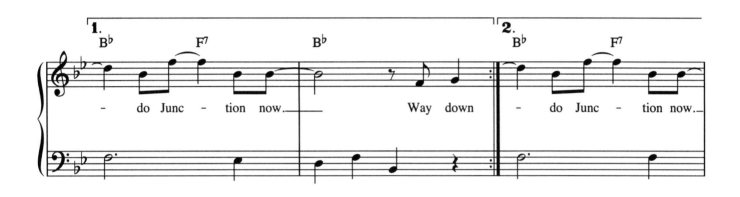

1. – do Junc – tion now.＿＿ Way down

2. – do Junc – tion now.

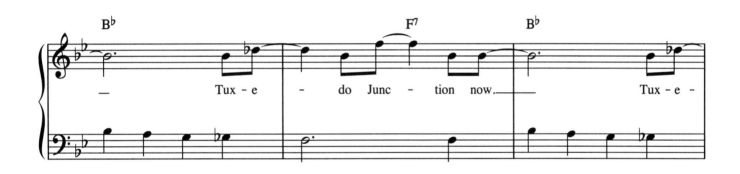

＿ Tux – e – do Junc – tion now.＿＿ Tux – e –

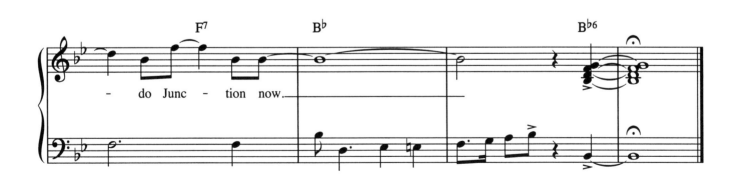

– do Junc – tion now.＿＿＿＿

You Make Me Feel So Young

Words by Mack Gordon. Music by Josef Myrow

Moderately

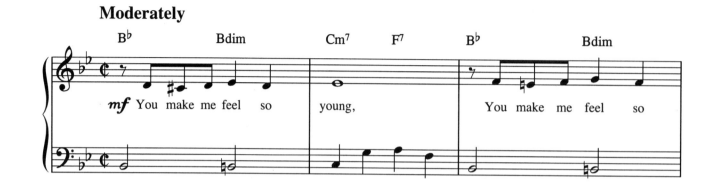

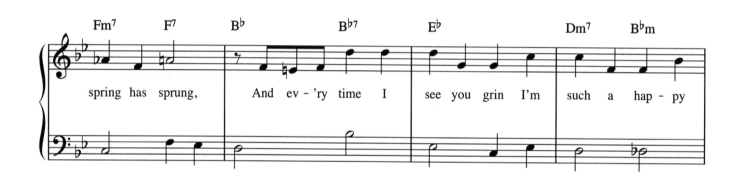

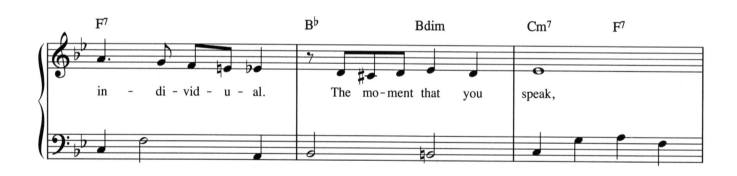

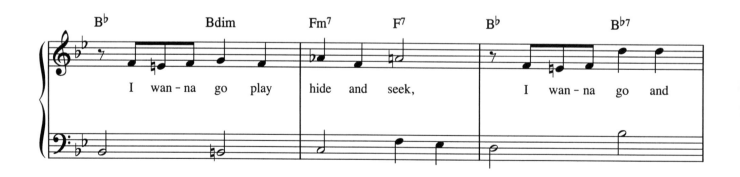

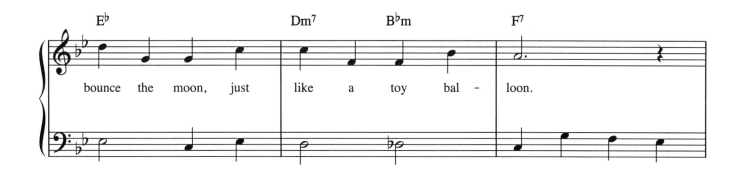

bounce the moon, just like a toy bal - loon.

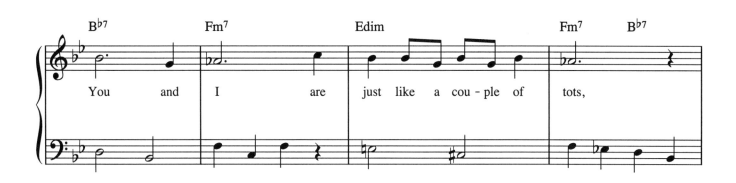

You and I are just like a cou - ple of tots,

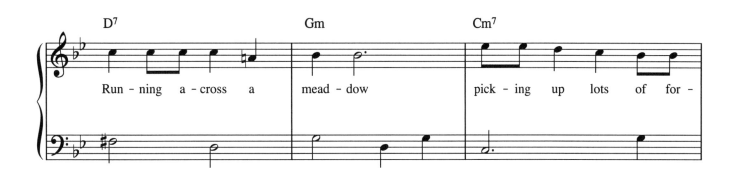

Run - ning a - cross a mead - dow pick - ing up lots of for -

get - me - nots. You make me feel so young. You make me feel there are

songs to be sung, bells to be rung, And a won – der – ful fling to be

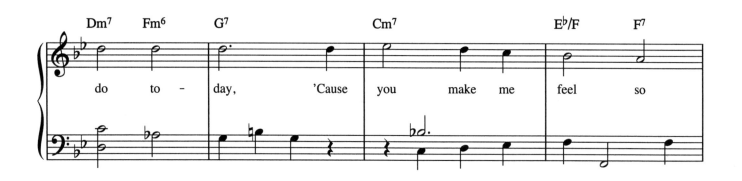

flung, And e – ven when I'm old and grey, I'm gon – na feel the way I

do to – day, 'Cause you make me feel so

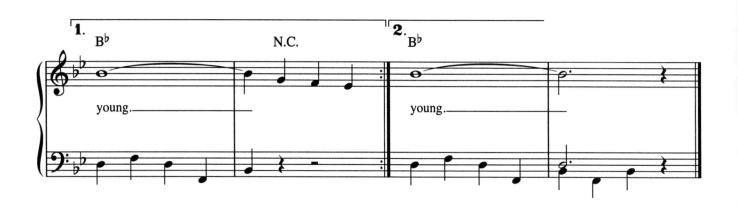

1.

young.

2.

young.